13 Ghost S
From Wl

Blackburns Yard, Whitby.

Produced by
The Cædmon Story Tellers
And
The Original Ghost Walk
With financial assistance from
Yorkshire & Humberside Arts
© **1999**

Apparitions both before and after death are, of course not infrequent in Whitby. Many a valuable house has stood untenanted for years on the suspicion of its being haunted; the last residents having experienced considerable alarm and anxiety; the bed clothes torn off, the china broke, and furniture demolished.

Strange traditions exist of certain yards, lanes and alleys; of some terrible homicide there committed: of departed spirits which have there walked for several nights successively, deprived of their rest, desirous of being addressed by someone, but none daring.

The Whitby Repository, 1828.

Collected together in these pages you will find Whitby ghost stories, old and new, told or retold by Michael Wray. The stories are complemented with fine wood cut prints by noted artist Anne Marshall.

Some of these stories can be heard on the Original Ghost Walk, others are whispered in dark corners of the ancient inns of the town......some none dare speak of at all!

Contents

The Silk Shawl

The Barguest Coach

Old Lisa

The Bells of St Hilda

The Whispering Ghost

The Grinning Donkey

The Eastern Lighthouse

The Whitby Puppeteer

The Burning Girl

Goosey's Ghost

Brown Bushell

The Barguest

The Wicked Punch & Judy Man

The Silk Shawl

Like most sea ports, Whitby has had its share of pirates and cut-throats down the centuries. Once a particularly unpleasant pirate worked out of Whitby. He was unpleasant not just in his form of piracy (his boat was made to look like a vessel in distress, and his cruel crew would over power and kill everyone on board any ship that came to give assistance) but he was also extremely ugly. The pirate would have been a big broad man had he not had very short legs. His legs were so short that people called him "Old Gravel Arse" - but never if he could hear them, for he was incredibly strong and cruel, with huge hairy hands. His face was pockmarked, and his eyes - which were of different sizes - appeared to be gazing at two different objects at the same time. Perhaps the strangest thing about the pirate was his wife, who was as beautiful as he was ugly. Some people said that Old Gravel Arse had come to an agreement with the devil in order to win her hand in marriage, but the truth was less dramatic. The girl came from a very poor background, and despised her poverty. She realised that the pirate, no matter how ugly, could provide her with the luxurious lifestyle she craved, and so much to everyone's surprise but her own, she allowed him to woo and wed her within a week.

The two could be seen on market days, arm in arm - she dressed in her good boots and fine clothing, looking down on his balding head; he swaggering proudly, scowling furiously at any man who dared to gaze at his wife's lovely face.

Once the door of their cottage was closed behind them, a remarkable change occurred between the two. For in truth, like many women, she could not stand her husband. She treated him like a dog. Many times he went to sea with bruises on his head caused by her bashing him with a frying pan, and he dared not return from a voyage without some present or dainty tit-bit. If he ever did, she would curse and rave at him, accusing him of not loving her. This was her cruelest act, for whatever his faults (and he had many) the pirate loved her.

On one voyage the hen-pecked pirate boarded a boat that carried a female passenger. His wicked men hacked up the crew one by one with their cutlasses before throwing their bodies over the side. Finally they closed upon the girl, who flung her hands up, pleading for mercy. Old Gravel Arse noticed she was wearing a beautiful blue silk shawl, so he waved his crew back, and asked her to give it to him. As he held it up to the light, he imagined how fine it would look around the shoulders of his wife. He signalled his men again, and they hacked the poor woman up with their cutlasses, then threw her body into the sea. The pirate tenderly folded the shawl, and placed it in his breast pocket, occasionally taking it out during the long voyage, admiring it, imagining the blissful moment when his beautiful wife wrapped it around her shoulders for the first time.

Once more at home, Old Gravel Arse presented his wife with the silk shawl. For a second he shook with fear, for she inspected it closely, and seemed to realise it was second hand. But it was a lovely piece of material, and slowly a greedy smile spread over her face. She rushed into her dressing room to try it on. Timidly, Old Gravel Arse followed her, watching from the doorway as she sat on a little stool in front of the mirror, gazing adoringly at her own face before gathering up the shawl and throwing it over her shoulders. For a second she looked down to admire the intricate stitch work, then looked up to see how well it suited her.

A shriek of horror escaped her lips, for gazing out of the mirror she saw not her own face, but that of the original owner. That poor woman had been dead for some three weeks, and her face was not a pretty sight. It was white and swollen from being so long in the water, there were great gashes on her head where the pirates had attacked her, and great chunks of her nose and lips were missing, nibbled away by the fishes. Old Gravel Arse also saw the horrible sight in the mirror. Had he had the presence of mind to tell his wife that it was only the reflection that looked terrible, not her own face, he might have averted the tragedy that unfolded. For she, seeing the horrified look on his face, let out another, and more dreadful scream and ran out of the house, down to the river, where she threw herself in. He ran after her as quickly as his little legs would allow, but got to the water's edge too late: his wife's lifeless body was by then drifting out of the harbour mouth, only to be washed up some few weeks later looking rather like the ghastly image she had seen reflected in her own mirror.

The "Pirate's" Grave
St Mary's Churchyard

The Barguist Coach

At one time it was believed that if ever a sailor from Whitby died on land, then on the third night after his funeral a ghostly black coach, pulled by headless horses, would go into St Mary's church yard via Green Lane, and pull up beside the grave. After a moment, a number of ghastly skeletal mourners would descend from the coach. These ghosts had obviously been seaman during their lives for, in the green light they cast about them, rags of nautical attire could be seen. Tattered pea jackets hung on bony shoulders, while here and there a rusty naval cutlass would clank against a mouldy hip bone. Even the ghost of a ship's cook was present, his wooden leg, riddled with ship worm, clicking against neighbouring head stones. The ghostly mourners, after walking round the grave three times, would summon up the dead man, and he would emerge from the ground, shrunken and yellowed like ancient parchment.

By now the headless horses were impatiently stamping their hooves, churning up the turf, so the mourners and their recently exhumed companion would climb into the coach. It would then rattle down the church steps, turn up Henrietta Street and plunge over the cliff into the sea.

The explanation for all this nocturnal activity given in those days was that the souls of sailors must dwell with their comrades beneath the waves until the day of judgment arrived.

Today we live in a more rational time, and a couple of theories have developed to explain away this supernatural tale. The first theory is that the legend was invented by parents and smugglers to discourage children from looking out of their windows at night. Since most people in Whitby were involved in, or profited by, smuggling, they had good reason to deter their children from learning too much, or asking awkward questions.

The other theory relates to actual events which occurred in St Mary's church yard in the 18th century. It was the fashion amongst the rich folk of the area at that time, to hold funerals at night, adding a dramatic twist to that sombre business. It is suggested that children saw torches flickering in the church yard, heard the clatter of horses hooves, and so a sinister legend evolved to explain these sights and sounds.

It is impossible now to find out which (if either) of these theories is right. If you have the courage, however, it is perfectly possible, to find out whether the legend itself has a basis in fact. Next time you hear of an aged sailor passing away, wait three days after the funeral has passed, then make your way at nightfall to the graveyard on Scarborough Road (St Mary's was closed for burials in 1858), and wait through the night by the grave side. If you are lucky, you may be rewarded by the sight of a black coach pulled by headless black horses, filled with ragged leering skeletons, summoning up a yellowed corpse by your feet.

Good luck to you!

**Fortune's Kipper House,
Henrietta Street**

Old Lisa

For many years after the death of "Old Lisa", St Mary's church yard, at the top of the 199 steps, was closed on April 24th, St Mark's eve. Anyone peering over the walls after sunset on this day would see lanterns glinting here and there, as the wardens patrolled the grounds to prevent anyone from getting in. A careful observer might notice that the patrolling wardens went round the church only in a clockwise direction, fearful of seeing what "Old Lisa" had seen many years before.

Old Lisa, was one of the "wise women" or witches of the town, and had been in the custom of visiting the church on this hallowed evening. She would shuffle her way three times round the building in an anti-clockwise direction, and then wait in the porch until midnight, for it was believed that the souls of those who are to die in the following year would then appear. No other person in the town dared to visit the church on this night, and as a result, Old Lisa was held in great reverence. Time after time folk would try to get her to pass on word of who was to die over the year, but she would twist her moustached lips together and keep her counsel, mumbling only, "I knows what I knows."

It was one of her great pleasures in life to nod sagely at the funeral of one of her neighbours and say, "I knew, of course."

Though many held her in great awe, believing she had some supernatural knowledge, some of the younger townsfolk doubted her, pointing out that anyone could be as wise as Lisa, predicting a death - after the event.

One St Mark's eve saw a great change in Old Lisa. For many years the fishermen, who are by nature superstitious, had paid the old witch a weekly retainer, a few pennies or so, fearing that she would curse their fishing if they failed to do so. But this particular year, after her habitual visit to the church yard, she began to refuse the payments, telling them to treat themselves to a pint of ale at "The Board" instead. They would try to force their payment on her, but she would shake her head and hobble away, muttering, "I knows what I knows..." She even knitted some warm socks for the single men!

The children in Liza's yard, who had once rushed by her house in terror of the old crone, were now likely to see her sitting on her doorstep, peeling spuds, or shelling the peas she grew on her steep cliff side garden. They never went past that summer without her presenting them with some treat - a boiled sweet, a handful of her succulent peas, or a new dress for a favourite doll. Soon it came to be that if a child fell and cut its knee, it would run for comfort to Old Lisa rather than to its own mother.

As winter drew on, less was seen of Old Lisa. She would be seen on a Sunday going up the stairs to St Mary's church, or occasionally visiting one of her poorer neighbours, giving them blankets to "keep the bairns warm", or other thoughtful presents.

Then in midwinter, an epidemic of pneumonia broke out and swept through the town. The funeral bell rang often from the church at the top of the stairs. Old Lisa disappeared into her house, and was not seen for over a week. The local children became curious, and began to peek through her key hole. They told their parents that she could be seen on her knees, hands uplifted, muttering prayers.

As spring came on, the cruel epidemic passed, and another change in Lisa's behaviour became apparent. The children had begun to play out again, and naturally they played by the house where they had been so welcome the year before. Old Lisa would rush out of the house with a black scowl on her face, telling them to get back to their own yards or doorsteps. When she passed the single fisherlads she would jab an accusing finger towards their feet, muttering that she hadn't been paid yet.

The day before St Mark's Eve, Old Lisa was walking down Henrietta Street. She was doing the rounds gathering up the "presents" she had given out the previous year. One of the neighbours, who she had until recently treated with kindness, stopped her by the foot of the 199 steps to ask if she would be going up to St Mary's the following evening. Lisa scowled at the intrusion, but then grinned and shook her head. "No," she said, "It's all nonsense you know. Guess who I saw leading off the souls last year, you'll never guess. Now I know it's all nonsense."

And thus muttering she turned to go. She had only gone a few yards when the brewery dray horse, delivering to the Board Inn, took sudden fright and galloped down the road, crushing Old Lisa beneath the iron-rimmed cart wheels. Passers by rushed to her, but there was no saving the old woman. She had only time to gasp, "Lord save my soul, it's true".

And there on the street Old Lisa passed away.

The Bells of St Hilda

St Hilda founded an abbey at Whitby in 655 AD, and she was such an impressive woman that legends sprang up about her after her death.

For instance, it was believed that the ammonite fossils that you may find in the rocks around Whitby were the bodies of snakes which she had hurled from the cliff, the abbey having suffered a plague of these creatures.

Geese were also wonderfully influenced by St Hilda, and it was believed that they would fall to the ground as they passed the abbey as a sign of respect.

People said that the bells in her abbey were so sweet that they could calm storms, and that they eventually attracted the attention of pirates. These wicked pirates stole the lovely bells, but failed to make any money from their crime, as their boat sank shortly afterwards, the bells, the boat and the pirates lying to this day under the sea near Black Nab. The bells are said to ring under the water at Halloween, and anyone who hears them may call out the name of their true love, to guarantee that they will marry them within a year, to the joyful pealings of St Mary's bells.

The waters from the abbey well were supposed to have special properties, capable of curing all sorts of illnesses, and it is a little known fact that Whitby once had quite a reputation as a spa.

There are no pictures today to show us what St Hilda looked like, but you may wish to see her. If so, simply go to this well at twelve-o-clock on a dark and moonless night, peer down into it, and you are sure to see her face looking back up at you - as long as you've been good, that is. Wicked people are confronted with the face of the Devil, and carried off to Hell.

The Old Spa, Bagdale Terrace

The View From Cædmon's Rest,
Church Street.

The Whispering Ghost

John Wesley, the founder of the Methodist Church, visited Whitby 11 times between 1761 and the year before his death in 1791. A little known fact about him is that he had a pet poltergeist or ghost, known affectionately as "Old Geoffrey", who haunted his fathers vicarage on the Isle of Axeholme in Lincolnshire.

Old Geoffrey was generally a harmless sprite, and except for rattling cupboard doors in the night, would not cause trouble just as long as the Wesleys remembered to set a place for him at the dinner table, and did not accidently lock him in any rooms within the house. Many of John Wesley's letters to his sister mention the ghost, enquiring after his health, Etc, and he appears to have felt some affection for it.

This affection was obviously returned by Old Geoffrey, for when Wesley died, the ghost disappeared from his home in Lincolnshire, and began to visit different chapels around the country, throwing open cupboard doors, emptying drawers onto the floor, as if searching for his friend. Eventually he arrived in Whitby, at the chapel which Wesley had opened the year before his death.

"It was very providential" Wesley wrote, "that part of the adjoining mountain fell down and demolished our old preaching house, with many houses besides; by which means we have one of the most beautiful chapels in Great Britain, finely situated on the steep side of the mountain." He went on, ".... in all England, I have not seen a more affectionate people than those of Whitby."

Perhaps it was because Wesley felt so happy in Whitby that Old Geoffrey decided to set up home here. He used to haunt the porch of the old chapel, whispering encouragement to people to enter in such a tiny voice that they thought it was their own conscience - though he was reported as pushing some visitors through the doors when they showed reluctance to enter, and occasionally he joined in the singing of hymns, badly out of tune. Sadly, the congregation were not very keen on Old Geoffrey, and he abandoned them, moving to the Primitive Methodist Chapel in what the locals cruelly called "Ranters Yard", referring to the enthusiasm of the preachers there. Sadly for the ghost, the Primitive Methodist's numbers declined, and their church eventually closed, making poor "Old Geoffrey" homeless.

Today he hangs around outside the doors of pubs in the town, so that gentlemen passing hear a tiny voice, so quiet that they think it is their own conscience urging them to enter. (That's what I tell my wife, anyway.) Sometimes

Old Geoffrey, lonely since the closing of the chapel, enters the pub himself, and the landlords, realising that they will have problems if they accidently lock him in, keep serving until the midnight hour is passed. (That's what the landlords tell the Police anyway.)

The Old Town Hall
The Original Ghost Walk
starts here at 8 pm

The Grinning Donkey

Until recent times, there were no donkey rides on Whitby's west beach - only ponies were employed for this purpose. No one in Whitby would even sit upon the back of a donkey. This local peculiarity was not out of pride, but of fear - fear at what had happened back in the days when the Reverend Lionel Charlton had established a school in the old town hall.

Now in those days the only route from Whitby to Sandsend was the beach, and it is a hard walk between the two.

Fortunately it was not always necessary to walk. An old couple, the Haywards, set up a little business transporting people and goods between the two places. They lived in a little shack of a house along the beach near Sandsend, an old place which fell into the sea during the 1930's.

Most mornings Mr Hayward would lead his six donkeys along the beach to Whitby, while his wife would take the other half dozen to Sandsend. Here they would sit all day, hiring out the animals at a penny a time, making their money and biding their time.

The children of the town took a particular pleasure in tormenting Mr Hayward, for he talked to himself, and was forever picking great bogies from his nose. They shouted names at him, and threw stones at the donkeys to make him chase them. Old Hayward was no runner though, for he was particularly fond of strong drink, but he would shake his fist and yell curses at the children, promising that one day they'd be sorry for making his life a misery. So fond of his drink was the old fellow, that sometimes he was not fit to walk on to Whitby in the morning. On these occasions his wife would send the donkeys off to Whitby by themselves, collecting the money from travellers when they arrived in Sandsend. (This was not as foolish as it may sound, for donkeys are intelligent, cunning animals, and could actually do their part of the business better by themselves than with Mr Hayward's help.)

One winter's day, believing that the freezing December air was good for developing character in children, Mr Charlton took his class to the West beach for a natural history lesson.

On this day, Mr Hayward was absent, the donkeys standing untended by the pier. The animals shifted about nervously as the class, which contained every nasty boy and girl in the town, swarmed down onto the beach. Despite the reverend's best efforts, some of the little rogues began to throw objects at the poor animals, who eventually trotted off to a safe distance. Looking round, the boys noticed one donkey had not run away. This creature was a dark, mangy thing, with half-bald ears, and huge yellow teeth. It turned it's head towards the children, and seemed to be grinning mockingly at them. The boys shouted vile abuse at it, but instead of running away, the donkey trotted towards them in a friendly manner. They threw stones at it, but the grinning donkey didn't seem to mind. One of them ran towards it and jumped onto its back, and it trotted along with him. Another ran and leapt on too, the donkey seemed content. Another joined them, then another, and strange to say, there was still room for more. Soon every nasty child in the class was sitting on the donkey, whose back had mysteriously stretched to twenty feet long! Then it turned its head to the sea, and galloped full tilt into the waves. The children were too afraid to jump off, and were carried away into the water, screaming like demented sea gulls, never to be seen again.

After this unfortunate incident the school closed down, and no one in Whitby would ever again set foot upon a donkey's back (so to speak). As a result, Poor Mr Hayward went bust, and ended his days in the workhouse. His wife, however, ran away with a rich glue maker from Darlington, and lived in luxury for many years.

The Church Steps, Whitby.

A Map Of Whitby

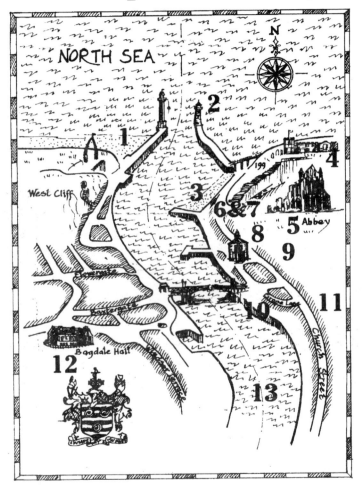

NORTH SEA

N

West Cliff

1

2

199

4

3

6&7

8

5 Abbey

9

11

10

Church Street

Bagdale Hall

12

13

Showing Ghostly Sites
& Worthwhile Haunts

1   West Beach. The Grinning Donkey.

2   The Eastern Lighthouse.

3   Tate Hill Sands. The Wicked Punch & Judy Man.

4   The Barguest Coach, St Mary's Church Yard.

5   St Hilda, the Abbey.

6   The Duke of York. Good food, good company, brilliant sea views, but watch out for the ghastly phantom that haunts the doorway on busy nights!

7   The Board Inn. Full of local charm and character. Stunning sea views. On a dark night from here, so it is said, the ghosts of two fishermen can be seen rowing into the harbour, their hands worn down to the bone as they row for eternity.

8   The Whispering Ghost. Still haunts the doorway of the Methodist Chapel.

9   The Black Horse. A truly traditional Whitby hostelry, reputedly the meeting between Pickering and the wandering puppeteer occurred here. Sit down, and drink - soon enough the tales and the ghosts will float before your senses!

10   The Burning Girl, Grape Lane.

11   The Endeavour. Panoramic harbour views, family room, and good Whitby company . Sit in the window seat and watch the ghosts go by.

12   Brown Bushell haunts Bagdale Hall.

13   Watch out for Goosey's Ghost at twilight.

The Eastern Lighthouse

The old lighthouses on the Whitby piers were built in 1833. They are made of a local, very hard, sandstone, and both are said to be haunted.

The lighthouse on the West Pier has been open as a tourist attraction since the pier extensions were built during the first world war, and thousands of people have climbed the steep staircase to the top to admire the view. Occasionally a one-armed figure appears on the steps of the western lighthouse, said to be the ghost of a local man who lost his left arm in an accident on the cliffs, gathering gulls' eggs.

The Eastern Lighthouse, however, has never been opened as a tourist attraction, nor was the eastern pier a popular place for visitors to stroll. The locals often congregated near the lighthouse when boats were late in returning, hoping to catch sight of a sail on the horizon.

At one time there were two brothers Peter and John, regarded as the best fishermen in the town. Only two years seperated the young men, and one summer, both took notice of a seventeen year old girl, by the name of Sylvia Swales. Both tried to court her, and she, flattered by their attentions, encouraged them both, equally. Her father was a practical man, however, and knowing that youth's charms do not last forever, and that life is hard, decided that he would choose which of the brothers should marry his daughter. He did this by measuring the quantity of fish they landed, reasoning that, as both brothers shared a steady and resolute character, the best provider should be the victor.

Throughout that summer and into the autumn, both lads worked hard on their boats, landing record catches on the old fish pier market (now the lifeboat pier), but neither gained an advantage over the other. Finally, on Christmas Eve, the old man made a decision: he who brought in the biggest catch that day would marry his daughter.

Before dawn both lads set sail amidst cheers from the other fishermen who, though they were having a holiday, got up early to see them off. Soon the sturdy cobles disappeared over the horizon as they raced to their favourite haunts.

As sunset approached, people began to gather excitedly on the east pier, expecting to see the boats return. The lighthouse beacon was lit, and the light glinted through an ever darkening sky. As the minutes passed, the waiting crowd fell into an expectant hush until two sails were sighted, passing the Runswick headland, three miles to the north of Whitby. Soon the boats were clearly seen, gunnels almost submerged by the vast weight of fish on board.

When the tide is running down the coast, great care is needed for a sailing vessel to enter Whitby harbour. There is always a danger of being pushed onto the deadly shoal of rocks known as the Scaur beyond the east pier, and it was even more dangerous in that time, before the pier extensions were built. Both men were more than ready to meet this challenge, however, and kept well over to the left as they neared the safety of the piers.

Now people began to cheer excitedly, and the lads, maybe sensing the spirit, began to race each other, forgetting for a moment the true aim of their mission. John, the younger brother, taking a few more risks, got ahead. At this point, Sylvia, who had never previously expressed a preference, knew her heart, and shouted, "Come on Peter!"

Now perhaps it was some freak of nature and her voice carried over the water clear over the noise of the crowd, or perhaps there was some other explanation, but at that moment, John threw up his hands from the tiller of his boat, and threw himself into the sea, the strong current dragging him away. Without a moment's hesitation, Peter turned his boat to attempt a rescue. The people on the pier groaned and cried as they saw the coble overturn on the scaur, throwing Peter into the water with his brother. Despite the gallant attempts of the townsfolk to throw out lines, the brothers were washed away and drowned, their battered bodies fetching up on Saltwick Nab a few days later.

Sylvia never married, and forever blamed herself for the death of her lovers. In later life she could be seen standing for hours on end by the old lighthouse, looking out to sea, as if hoping they would return.

The story of this tragedy was retold so often, that even while Sylvia lived, people began to believe it was a legend, the figment of some story teller's imagination, and Sylvia's strange behaviour led her to be mocked by the children of the town.

At the time of writing the old east pier is

inaccessible except at low tide, when care must be taken not to get stranded, so it is unlikely that you will visit the lighthouse or hear the strange sounds that are sometimes heard thereabouts. Maybe it is only a freak of nature, the sound of the wind whistling round the lighthouse making a sound like a voice calling "Peter", or perhaps there is some other explanation.

The Whitby Puppeteer

On the wintry morning of December 10th 1710, a puppeteer arrived in Whitby, intending to perform his "Incredible Motion" that evening. He hired a room near the market, set up the show, then posted handbills round the town to let people know that he would begin at 7.30pm.

Having some hours to spare, our puppeteer decided to visit a local hostelry now known as the Black Horse, and setting himself in a corner listened, fascinated, to the fabulous yarns spun by the locals there. A local rogue named William Pickering was also present. He had no stories to tell, but shouted, "that's the way to do it" at the puppeteer, in the high squeeky voice which the second rate travelling Punch and Judy men used, thus mocking his profession. The puppet master was rather upset, for he was a sensitive man, who had once had ambitions to "tread the boards" of the London theatres, and his shows were noted for their genteel quality and high moral tone. He left the bar in a foul mood, leaving Pickering to gloat.

Now the drunkard Pickering had spent all his money on beer, but deciding he wanted to watch the show, sneaked into the room shortly after it had started. He tiptoed loudly down to the front, where he squeezed rudely between two young ladies who had paid good money for their seats, and there he sat grinning lewdly at them and loudly muttering "that's the way to do it." The puppeteer was obviously enraged but tried to continue. However, as two puppet lovers met in a tender kiss, Pickering belched loudly, which proved the last straw for the puppet master. He rushed out upon Pickering, pulling out the large dagger he always carried for protection. He lunged at Pickering's chest, but the fortunate drunkard threw up his arm just in time, deflecting the murderous blow. The blade pierced instead the heart of one of the pretty young girls at his side. For a second there was a horrified silence in the lamp lit room, followed by groans and screams.

He fled from the room, and ran through the market place, the bloody dagger still gripped tightly in his hand, and succeeded in hiding himself beneath a pile of stinking crab pots, hoping to escape once the streets were quiet. During the long cold night the face of the poor girl appeared before him over and over again, and as dawn came, in remorse, he surrendered himself to the town constable.

He was tried in York, and pleaded guilty to murder, even though he was told the court would accept a plea of manslaughter. The judge had no choice other than to condemn him to death, and he was hanged outside the walls of

York. His body, as was then the custom, was returned to Whitby, and displayed in a *gibbet*, a little cage hung from the top of a pole at a place called Spital Bridge, at the end of Church Street. After ten years, what remained of his body was buried outside the town, at a place until recently known as Gallows Close.

It is said that the ghost of the puppeteer is sometimes seen running through the market place, dressed all in black, carrying his bloody weapon. Any man who sees this ghost is advised to avoid it: he who catches sight of its face, still contorted with the horror of the black deed, is plunged into insanity.

To this day the Black Horse remains the haunt of yarn spinning drunkards, and a gibbering refuge for those who have had the misfortune to meet the puppeteer's frightful gaze!

The Burning Girl

On Grape Lane stands a house which used to serve as an infirmary for the people of the town. It is a pretty street, but not one on which you would be wise to linger alone at twilight, sniffing the evening air.

In 1917, a local girl by the name of Mary Clarke, was sent to the local baker with her father's dinner. It was normal in those days to send food to the bakers for cooking in the summer, to save on fuel.

The girl was well known in the town for her good looks and her beautiful long golden hair, which she brushed, morning and evening, one hundred times, dabbing in a drop of "Dr Firth's Patent Hair Oil" until it shone like burnished gold.

The baker, being busy, told the girl to put the food into the oven herself, and to his horror saw a lock of her hair fall into the flames. In an instant her whole head was on fire.

In a panic she ran out of the shop, the wind fanning the flames, and in seconds her clothes were burning too.

The baker raced from the shop, but could not catch her before she had been dreadfully burnt. He managed to beat out the flames, then walked with her to the old hospital which stood on Grape Lane. With each step, lumps of her burnt skin dropped off, providing a tasty snack to the dogs of the town, who apparently followed the rich cooking smell flocking round her, howling and wagging their tails.

Within an hour the poor girl died, apparently only worried about the state of her hair. Occasionally, in the evening, the ghost of that poor girl appears on Grape Lane. At first a flame appears floating by itself, then the figure of the girl is seen, along with the crackling of flames and the howling and slavering of hungry dogs. For a second the ghost pauses and stares into the beholders eyes then passes on, trailing a rich smell of cooking behind her.

No one who has ever met this tragic figure is ever able to eat roast lamb again.

In the 1930's, the Endeavour public house, which stands near the end of Grape Lane, was burned to the ground, the family escaping safely when the mother was woken in the dead of night by a dream or premonition of a beautiful blonde haired girl shaking her, and warning her to save her children. Although rebuilt twice since then, the building is still said to be haunted.

Goosey's Ghost

The big yellow dredger that periodically scrapes the mud and silt from Whitby harbour is of vital importance to the town. Without it, the deep water facilities which allow great steel barges to unload here would quickly disappear. After a while the trawlers would only be able to land their fish at high tide, and Bell Isle, a stinking mud flat which used to stand in the middle of the upper harbour would slowly reappear. The river would slow down, and the fields between Whitby and Ruswarp would flood at every tide, becoming waterlogged and full of reeds, the landscape taking on the appearance it would have presented to a visitor a few hundred years ago.

The noise the traveller would have heard, had he rowed a boat up the river through the maze of muddy channels in the autumn, would have been that of thousands of geese, honking discordantly: for the river in those days provided an excellent overnight spot for migrating geese. Now at that time the flesh of the goose was highly sought after, particularly that of the Barnacle Goose, and for this reason: it was the only bird that could be eaten on a Friday. The Barnacle Goose breeds in Greenland far to the north of Britain, and no one back then had ever seen a barnacle goose egg. It was believed that this bird grew out of barnacles, was really a fish, and could be eaten on Fridays.

At one time a man lived in the town who was so fond of this dish that he was given the name of "Goosey" by his friends. Goosey had a large stomach, but a small brain and he attempted to make money out of his belly by betting his friends £20 that he could eat an entire goose within an hour. The bet being accepted, a goose was captured and cooked. Goosey sat down and began to eat with relish, gulping down the breasts within a few minutes. Next he gnawed on the wings, then he turned his attention to the legs. Sweat began to trickle down his neck, and his steady munching rhythm faltered. Goosey was having problems. However, with fifteen minutes to spare, he had finished the legs, stripped the little bits of meat to be found on the bird's back, and he had only one small piece to eat.

The one small piece Goosey had still to eat was the bit called the parson's nose, or what you might call the bum. The bum of a goose is a particularly unattractive morsel, made up of knobbly skin, fat and gristle. The bum of a cooked goose, after cooling for 45 minutes, tastes something like a cross between a dirty sock and toenails, and has the texture of an old rubber glove which has been left in riverside mud to rot for a month. Goosey manfully chewed on a piece of the parson's nose, but could not force himself to swallow. He turned an interesting shade of green, and eventually admitted defeat, spitting out the horrible lump. He gave his friends £20, which they shared out in triumph.

Goosey was upset, not just because he had lost £20, but because he had a certain pride in the capacity of his belly. Feeling the honour of his stomach had been tarnished, it did not take long before he decided to set matters right by offering the same bet to his friends again.

Now Goosey's friends were aware that Goosey would have been practising his eating for the second contest, and agreed to the bet only on the condition that they should provide the goose. On the agreed day, the bird was brought to Goosey's house. It was an huge old grandad of a beast, the skin tough and scaly, more gristle than flesh. Goosey was confident however, and had it wrapped entirely in streaky bacon and filled with onions to prevent the flesh drying out in the cooking.

Now his friends had been correct in suspecting that Goosey had been practising his eating, but he also had a secret strategy: when the goose was cooked, Goosey began to eat the parson's nose first, leaving the tenderest, tastiest, portions till last.

With plenty of time to spare, Goosey had chomped through the bum, legs and wings, before polishing off the moist breasts - even crunching the bacon, before triumphantly grabbing a slice of bread to sop up the gravy. Proudly he tilted his head back and dropped the dripping bread straight into his throat, before patting his belly contentedly.

Exactly how Goosey died is now shrouded in the mists of time. Some people say that he choked on the bread, others that he burst his full belly by patting it, but however it happened, within an hour of his triumph, Goosy was dead.

Today if you row up the river from Whitby

to Ruswarp, you will not need to navigate past Bell Isle, or risk getting lost in the maze of mud channels that once formed the River Esk. Nor will you hear the call of wild geese - unless you happen to be on the river at about sunset, when occasionally the ghost of poor Goosey is seen. He appears in the form of a solitary goose, glowing faintly green and honking in a melancholic sort of way.

Brown Bushell

Bagdale Hall was once the abode of Brown Bushell, a man of great energy and what proved to be a fatal love of variety.

Had Bushell been born today, he could have changed jobs as often as he wanted, but sadly he was born in the seventeenth century, and was an officer in the Parliamentary army at the outbreak of the Civil War. Within a year he changed sides, commanding a ship for Charles I. After "borrowing" the vessel to fight for the king of Spain, he returned to England and offered his services to Parliament again.

Although he served Parliament with distinction for the rest of the war, he was afterwards arrested, tried for treason, and beheaded.

A man of great energy in life, his spirit showed the same zest after death, haunting the graveyard where his body was buried, his home in Whitby, and the wooded path known as Union Steps, between Whitby and Ruswarp, where his ghost was said to carry its head under its arm.

Brown Bushell's ghost was to be of great service to the sailors of Whitby during the Napoleonic wars, for the press-gang were afraid of ghosts, and would not enter the woods around the Union Steps, leaving the local mariners with an ideal refuge.

Brown Bushell's ghost has not been seen in the woods for many years, but is still a resident of Bagdale Hall, though not so active as he used to be.

When the house was bought by the Geoffries family in the early years of the twentieth century, Bushell was still causing great problems, knocking over furniture, slamming doors, and generally being a nuisance. His favourite trick was to terrify the younger maids, appearing headless in front of them before throwing their skirts over their heads. Shaw Geoffries, realising that the ghost had an eye for the ladies, thwarted him by employing two ugly and aged biddies, called Kate and Caroline, and in the presence of these unsightly crones, his activities declined.

Today Bushell's ghost haunts certain rooms at Bagdale Hall, casting a gloomy and brooding shadow over them. Although he does not do anything dramatic, people who have felt his presence in a room will never re-enter it, describing the feeling of the room as "deeply miserable", As if Brown Bushell, having lost his head in the seventeenth century, has lost his humour in the twentieth.

A View From
The Church Steps

The Barguest

For many hundreds of years, the most dreaded sound in Whitby was the howl of a certain dog - the Barguest hound. This animal was described as being large, black and fierce, with red flaming eyes, and his howl was a sure portent of death. In country areas the Barguest was sometimes said to tear its victims to pieces, but in the town, the howl of the beast signalled the imminent demise of either the hearer, or a member of their family by illness or other natural causes.

Not all barguests are man eaters, but all of them are unpleasant to meet. In the 19th century it is said that a local farmer succeeded in jumping on the back of one. It trotted along obediently for a while like a placid mare, but then abruptly halted in front of a pond. The farmer, taken by surprise, was catapulted into the stinking water, and the barguest disappeared with a mocking howl.

In 1951, archaeologists excavating a Roman signalling station at Kettleness, just north of Whitby, discovered the skeletons of a man and a huge dog lying curled together. The jaws of the creature nestled on the mans throat, and it was obvious these two had died fighting each other - the man had stabbed the dog with a sword, but the dog had ripped out his throat.

Historically, the Vikings and Celts trained large hounds to help them in battle, unleashing these ferocious beasts on their enemies.

A spate of Barguest sightings followed this grim discovery, as if the demon had been released, and continued until 1974, when a priest aptly named Daved Omen carried out an exorcism on the spot, much to the relief of the terrified inhabitants of Runswick.

Although the dreaded howl of the barguest is no longer heard in Whitby a great black dog can still be found in the town - Black Dog Ale, brewed locally and sold in a *popular haunt* - The Duke of York.

The Wicked
Punch & Judy Man

Had you come down onto the Tate Hill sands some fifty years ago, you might have seen a Punch & Judy show there, owned by an odd man named Professor Renfield. He was an old man who appeared in the area every spring, performing his show up and down the east coast throughout the summer, then disappearing mysteriously every autumn.

Even back then nobody could remember the first time the professor had performed in

Whitby, though the old folk seemed to recall that he had first appeared one morning after a dreadful storm had washed an old and deserted sailing vessel ashore on the beach.

Wherever he came from, his show proved to be the most popular the town had ever known. The action was fast, funny and furious, the puppets, people said, seemed almost alive.

The fact is the puppets were alive. Even worse, they were a family of vampire dwarfs, and once a week, as they performed their show, the family would look out at the audience to select a child who was a little plumper or more juicy looking than its playmates.

After the show the old professor, with the help of a bag of boiled sweets, would engage the chosen victim in conversation. He would find out where the child lived or was staying. After dark he would carry his vampire family there in a brightly painted barrow which barely made a noise as it slipped through the darkening streets. They would stop outside the abode of the sleeping victim..... the details of what would happen next are too horrible to describe.

For many years Professor Renfield travelled the east coast with his child-slaying family, no-one suspecting such a harmless looking old man could be behind the child disappearances which had mystified the police for many years.

But at last though, he was caught, stopped by a policeman on Sandgate whilst erratically wheeling his barrow, the vigilant officer correctly suspecting that the old fellow was drunk. An inspection of the barrow revealed the dwarfs, mouths smeared with blood, sucking at the severed limbs of their latest victim

They were all tried for murder and, except for Renfield, hanged at the gallows. The professor escaped the noose, but not a gruesome death. He died the day before the execution: the little vampires, who had been starved for over a month during their imprisonment, turned on their master, bit his throat out, and drained him of his blood.

Some people, however, say that Professor Renfield and Mr Punch actually escaped and are still murdering children to this day; they say that Punch pretended he didn't know how to put his head into the noose, so the hangman showed him, and was killed himself, but I think this is probably someone mixing up the Punch and Judy show with this true story. However, you will not go far wrong if you run away screaming from any Punch and Judy man who ever takes an interest in you, especially if he asks your address!